Christmas Maths

for ages 7–9

Andrew Brodie ✓

Content of the worksheets

The first section of the book (Worksheets 1–22) contains activities that are targeted towards Year 3, while the later pages (Worksheets 23–45) are targeted towards Year 4. However, you may decide to select any of the sheets to use with your own class, regardless of which year groups you have. The aim should be for pupils to be engaged in enjoyable activities that provide practice of mathematical skills and knowledge.

Year 3

Worksheet		Objective
1	How many?	Count larger collections by grouping them.
2	Odds and evens	Recognise odd and even numbers.
3	Advent square	Describe and extend number sequences.
4	Missing numbers	Find numbers that are one more, ten more, one less or ten less than other given numbers.
5	Is this fair?	Know addition facts.
6	Christmas lights	Know addition facts.
7	Christmas tree tables (1)	Begin to know the 3 times table and know by heart the 5 times table.
8	Christmas tree tables (2)	Begin to know the 4 times table and know by heart the 10 times table.
9	Colour by numbers	Read and write whole numbers to at least 1000.
10	Festive fractions	Recognise simple fractions and use them to find fractions of shapes and numbers.
11	Buying decorations with £1	Solve problems involving money including finding totals.
12	Change from £1	Solve problems involving money including finding totals and giving change.
13	How much?	Solve problems involving money including finding totals and understand and use £ and p notation.
14	Christmas measuring (1)	Draw and measure lines to the nearest half centimetre. (This worksheet is used in conjunction with Worksheet 15.)
15	Christmas measuring (2)	Draw and measure lines to the nearest half centimetre.
16	The shepherd's route	Recognise and use the four compass directions N, S, E, W.
17	Christmas Eve angles	Identify right angles in 2-D shapes and the environment.
18	Wrapping presents	Use units of time and solve problems involving time.
19	Christmas coordinates	Describe positions and directions.
20	Complete the pictures	Sketch the reflection of a simple shape.
21	Symmetrical tree	Sketch the reflection of a simple shape.
22	My symmetry picture	Sketch the reflection of a simple shape.

Year 4

Worksheet		Objective
23	**Order in the workshop (1)**	Read and write whole numbers to at least 10,000 in figures and words.
24	**Order in the workshop (2)**	Read and write whole numbers to at least 10,000 in figures and words.
25	**Christmas rounding (1)**	Round any positive integer less than 1,000 to the nearest ten or hundred.
26	**Christmas rounding (2)**	Round any positive integer less than 1,000 to the nearest ten or hundred.
27	**Crack the code (1)**	Know the doubles of all whole numbers up to 50.
28	**Crack the code (2)**	Know the corresponding halves of all the doubles of numbers up to 50.
29	**Crazy trees**	Know by heart multiplication facts for the three times table and begin to know multiplication facts for the six times table.
30	**Christmas tree tables**	Begin to know multiplication facts for the seven times table and know by heart the multiplication facts for the four times table.
31	**Ring out the bells**	Know by heart multiplication facts for the four times table and begin to know the six and eight times tables.
32	**Santa's little helpers**	Begin to know multiplication facts for the 9 times table.
33	**Fraction baubles**	Begin to relate fractions to division and find simple fractions, use fraction notation, understand decimal notation and to recognise the equivalence between the decimal and fraction forms of one half and one quarter and tenths.
34	**Parcel sorting (1)**	Calculate the area of rectangles and other simple shapes.
35	**Parcel sorting (2)**	Calculate the area of rectangles and other simple shapes.
36	**Label the presents**	Calculate the perimeter of rectangles and other simple shapes; classify polygons using criteria such as number of right angles.
37	**Christmas shopping (1)**	Use subtraction and addition to solve problems with money.
38	**Christmas shopping (2)**	Use addition, multiplication and division to solve problems with money.
39	**My December calandar**	Understand time on calendars; spell days of the week.
40	**December dates**	Understand time on calendars.
41	**Christmas stars**	Make patterns by translation and reflection.
42	**Finding triangles**	Solve mathematical puzzles.
43	**Finding pentagons**	Solve mathematical puzzles; describe and visualise 2D shapes.
44	**How many shapes?**	Solve mathematical puzzles.
45	**Christmas Su Doku**	Solve mathematical puzzles.

How many?

Name: **Date:**

1. How many Christmas trees do you estimate there are on this sheet?

2. Now count them and write down the number that you have found.

3. How many snowmen do you estimate there are on this sheet?

4. Now count them and write down the number that you have found.

Are you sure that you are right? You can check by putting the objects into groups of five, then counting them up in fives. The first group of five trees has been done for you.

Notes for teachers
Objective: Count larger collections by grouping them
This task provides valuable practice in both estimation and counting. Some children do not have effective strategies for counting. Counting by arranging the objects into groups of five is one method.

Odds and evens

Name:  Date:

Colour the presents yellow. Colour the Santas red.
Write odd or even in the spaces below.

1. The presents are in the squares with .... numbers.

2. The Santas are in the squares with .... numbers.

3. The units digit of an odd number is always

☐ or ☐ or ☐ or ☐ or ☐

4. The units digit of an even number is always

☐ or ☐ or ☐ or ☐ or ☐

Notes for teachers
Objective: Recognise odd and even numbers
After completing this task, most children will be able to understand that the units digit determines whether a number is odd or even.

worksheet 3

Advent square

1. Draw a small red circle in the first square. Count on two squares and draw another small red circle (this one will be in the third square).

   Do you think that if you keep doing this you will draw a red circle on the square for Christmas Day?

2. Draw a small green circle in the first square. Count on three squares and draw another small green circle.

   Do you think that if you keep doing this you will draw a green circle on the square for Christmas Day?

December

1	2	3	4	5	6	7
8	9	10	11	12	13	14
15	16	17	18	19	20	21
22	23	24	25	26	27	28
29	30	31				

Notes for teachers
Objective: Describe and extend number sequences
Make sure that the pupils draw quite small circles so that they will be able to continue the investigation by drawing circles in more colours. Extend this activity by asking the children to draw a blue circle in the first square, then to count on in fours. Can they predict whether Christmas Day will have a blue circle? Now try counting on in fives, sixes, sevens and eights.

Missing numbers

Name:

 Date:

This is part of a hundred square. Fill in the missing numbers.

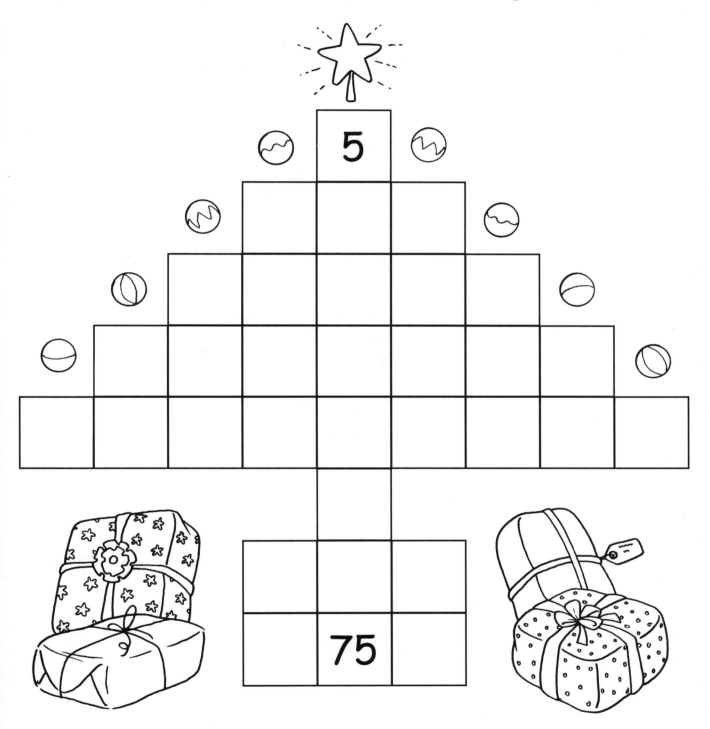

Notes for teachers
Objective: Find numbers that are one more, ten more, one less or ten less than other given numbers
Ensure that the children understand that this picture represents part of a hundred square. The children should be able to identify the relationships between numbers when 1 or 10 are added to them.

Worksheet 5

Is this fair?

Name:

 **Date:**

Granny gives two presents to Jordan and three presents to Jaz.

Grandad gives three presents to Jordan and two presents to Jaz.

 How many presents does Jordan have altogether from Granny and Grandad? ☐

 How many presents does Jaz have altogether from Granny and Grandad? ☐

They have the same because 2 + 3 = 3 + 2.

Here are six ways of making 5 by adding whole numbers:

4 + 1   3 + 2

1 + 4 — ⑤ — 0 + 5

2 + 3   5 + 0

Find ways to make 6.   Find ways to make 7.

⑥   ⑦

Notes for teachers
Objective: Know addition facts
This activity can be extended by asking the children to complete the same process for other numbers.

Christmas lights

Name: Date:

There are twelve lights on Joe's tree.

Joe only has red bulbs and green bulbs.

1. Colour one bulb red and eleven bulbs green.

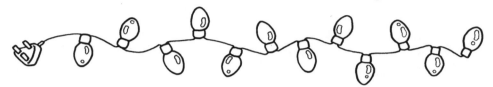

1 + 11 = 12

2. Colour two bulbs red and ten bulbs green.

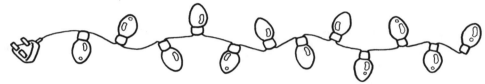

2 + 10 = 12

3. Now find some other ways to colour all the bulbs and write the sums that show these ways.

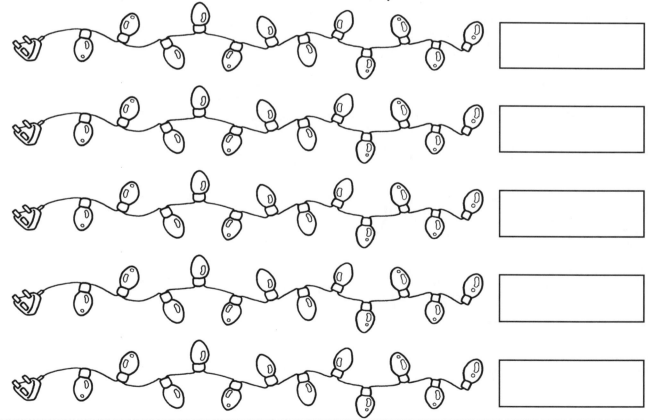

Notes for teachers
Objective: Know addition facts
Note that the colour order of the light bulbs is not relevant for this task. We are simply asking the children about the numbers of each colour of bulb.

Christmas tree tables (1)

Name:  **Date:**

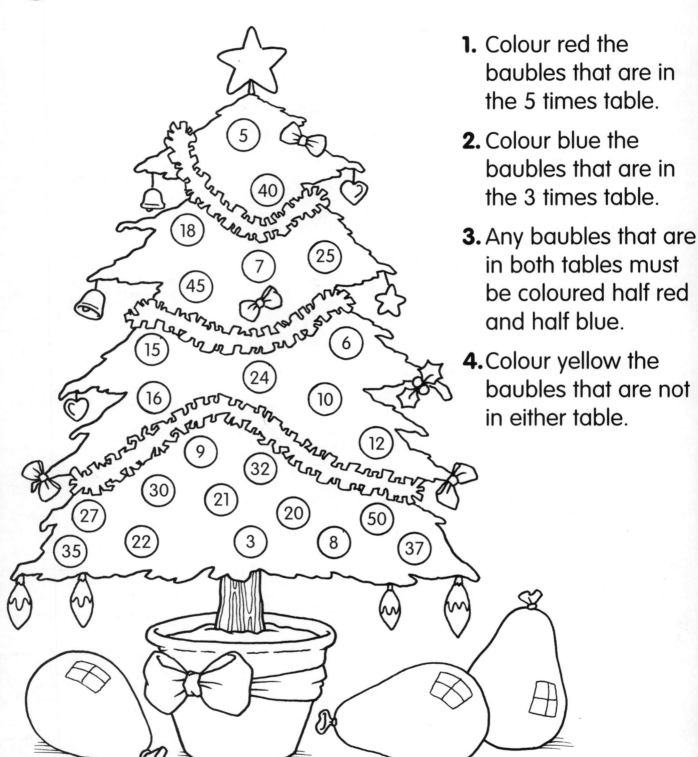

1. Colour red the baubles that are in the 5 times table.

2. Colour blue the baubles that are in the 3 times table.

3. Any baubles that are in both tables must be coloured half red and half blue.

4. Colour yellow the baubles that are not in either table.

Notes for teachers

Objective: Begin to know the 3 times table and know by heart the 5 times table
Encourage pupils to look for those that are in both tables first, to avoid problems with colouring. It may help pupils to write down the numbers from each table before they begin.

Christmas tree tables (2)

Name: **Date:**

1. Colour green the stars that are in the 10 times table.

2. Colour orange the stars that are in the 4 times table.

3. Any stars that are in both tables must be coloured half green and half orange.

4. Colour purple the stars that are not in either table.

Notes for teachers

Objective: Begin to know the 4 times table and know by heart the 10 times table.
Encourage pupils to look for those that are in both tables first, to avoid problems with colouring. It may help pupils to write down the numbers from each table before they begin.

Colour by numbers

Name:  Date:

Colour numbers between 1 and 99 blue.
Colour numbers between 100 and 299 red.
Colour numbers between 300 and 499 green.
Colour numbers between 500 and 699 yellow.
Colour numbers between 700 and 899 purple.
Colour numbers between 900 and 1000 orange.
Choose any other colours for unmarked spaces.

Notes for teachers
Objective: Read and write whole numbers to at least 1000
Encourage pupils to read the numbers aloud when thinking about what colour they should be.

Festive fractions

Name:

 Date:

Follow the instructions below to colour the correct number of items.

Colour $\frac{1}{2}$ of the parcels red. Colour $\frac{1}{2}$ of the parcels green.

Colour $\frac{1}{2}$ of the reindeer brown. Colour $\frac{1}{2}$ of the reindeer grey.

Colour $\frac{1}{4}$ of the chimneys black. Colour $\frac{1}{4}$ of the chimneys brown.

Colour $\frac{1}{2}$ of the chimneys red.

Colour $\frac{1}{3}$ of the stars yellow. Colour $\frac{2}{3}$ of the stars orange.

Colour $\frac{1}{3}$ of the coats blue. Colour $\frac{1}{3}$ of the coats red.

Colour $\frac{1}{3}$ of the coats purple.

Notes for teachers

Objective: Recognise simple fractions and use them to find fractions of shapes and numbers

An extension to this activity for the most able pupils would be to use quantities of smaller unit fractions. For instance, the ten parcels could have instructions based on fifths or tenths. You could use the same picture but change the instructions to make the activity more challenging.

Buying decorations with £1

Name:  Date:

50p 25p 36p 20p 70p

10p 24p 26p 30p 14p

How many different ways can you find to spend exactly £1 on decorations?

Record your ideas in any way that is easy to understand.
Here is one possibility:

1 angel (50p) + 2 x tinsel (2 x 25p) = £1

Notes for teachers
Objective: Solve problems involving money including finding totals
The challenge here is to reach exactly £1. Recording the results will be difficult for some children. They may like to record by drawing pictures as an alternative to using numbers and mathematical symbols.

Change from £1

Name:  **Date:**

Buy any 2 items and calculate how much change you would get from £1. You are not allowed to spend more than £1. Record your work in the table below.

Items bought		Total cost	Change from £1
angel 50p	angel 50p	£1	0p
bauble 20p	robin 26p	46p	54p

Notes for teachers
Objective: Solve problems involving money including finding totals and giving change
An extension could be to buy any 3 items and calculate the change.

How much?

Name:

 Date:

Work out the cost of the following decorations. Use the space to show how you have worked out your answer.

1. 2 angels and 3 pieces of tinsel

----

2. 5 baubles and 3 sprigs of holly

----

3. A set of lights and a candle

----

4. 10 candy canes and 2 robins

----

5. 10 santas

----

6. 1 snowman, 1 santa, and an angel

----

7. 1 of each item

50p

50p

50p

50p

10p

30p

36p

24p

26p

14p

Notes for teachers

Objective: Solve problems involving money including finding totals and understand and use £ and p notation
An extension to this activity would be to ask children to set each other the same type of questions. To do this they would have to have calculated the answers before giving their questions to another pupil to complete.

Christmas measuring (1)

Name:  **Date:**

Look at the picture on Worksheet 15

You will need to measure things carefully with a ruler to complete the statements below. Remember you are measuring the sizes of the pictures. In real life the items would be bigger!

1. The taller shepherd is .... cm tall

2. The shorter shepherd is .... cm tall

3. The star is .... cm high

4. The star is .... cm wide

5. The stable is .... cm high

6. The manger is .... cm high.

Now add the following items to the picture.

A sheep that is 3cm tall and $4\frac{1}{2}$ cm long.

A 7cm tall angel in the sky.

Mary and Joseph should be in the stable. Mary should be 7cm tall and Joseph should be $8\frac{1}{2}$ cm tall.

Notes for teachers
Objective: Draw and measure lines to the nearest half centimetre
This worksheet should be used in conjunction with Worksheet 15.

Worksheet 15

Christmas measuring (2)

Name: Date:

Notes for teachers

Objective: Draw and measure lines to the nearest half centimetre
You could extend this activity by increasing the number of items to be added to the picture or the items to be measured.

The shepherd's route

Name:  **Date:**

Follow the directions below to find the route the shepherd took to the stable. Use a ruler and a coloured pencil to mark the route you find on the map below.

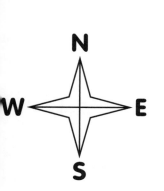

1. The shepherd walked 2 squares west.
2. He turned and walked 3 squares south.
3. He turned again and walked 2 squares east.
4. He turned again and walked 1 square south.
5. Next he walked 3 squares west.
6. After a short rest he walked 2 squares north.
7. He turned and walked 1 square west.
8. Finally he walked 2 squares south and found the baby Jesus in a manger.

Notes for teachers
Objective: Recognise and use the four compass directions N, S, E, W
An extension to this activity would be to ask the pupils to write a different return route for the shepherd using all four compass directions at least once.

Christmas Eve angles

Name:

 **Date:**

It is Christmas Eve and Santa has set out to begin his present delivery.

Look carefully at the picture below and see if you can see 10 right angles. Mark them clearly in a bright colour.

Notes for teachers
Objective: Identify right angles in 2-D shapes and Eve environment
Ensure pupils have a clear concept of what a right angle is before beginning this task.

Wrapping presents

Name:  Date:

1. Erin started wrapping this present at 2.25. She finished wrapping it at 2.40. How many minutes did it take for Erin to wrap the present?

 mins

2. Nathan started wrapping this present at 2.45. He finished wrapping it at 3.05. How many minutes did it take for Nathan to wrap the present?

[   ] mins

3. Charlotte started wrapping this present at 3.10. She finished wrapping it at 3.20. How many minutes did it take for Charlotte to wrap the present?

 mins

4. Charlotte stopped for a cup of tea after wrapping that present. She started wrapping presents again at 3.45. How long was Charlotte's tea break?

 mins

Notes for teachers
Objective: Use units of time and solve problems involving time
Encourage the children to use a simple time line to solve these questions – this will prepare them well for more difficult time questions in the future.

Christmas coordinates

Name: **Date:**

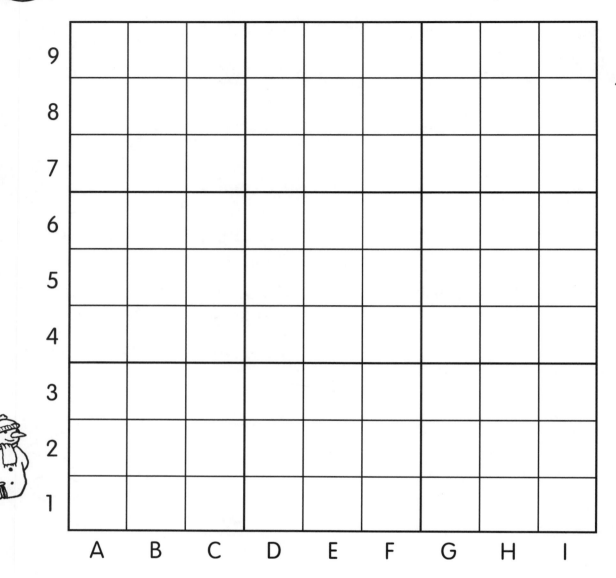

1. Colour in green: A4 B4 C4 D4 E4 F4 G4 H4 I4 B5 C5 D5 E5
F5 G5 H5 C6 D6 E6 F6 G6 D7 E7 F7 E8

2. Colour in brown: E3

3. Colour in red: D1 E1 F1 D2 E2 F2

4. Put a star in E9

....

Notes for teachers
Objective: Describe positions and directions
This worksheet provides an excellent opportunity to teach children the need to read the 'x coordinate' first.

Andrew Brodie: Christmas Maths 7–9 © A & C Black Publishers Ltd. 2006

Complete the pictures

Name:  Date:

Look carefully at the pictures below. Only half of each symmetrical picture has been drawn. Complete each picture.

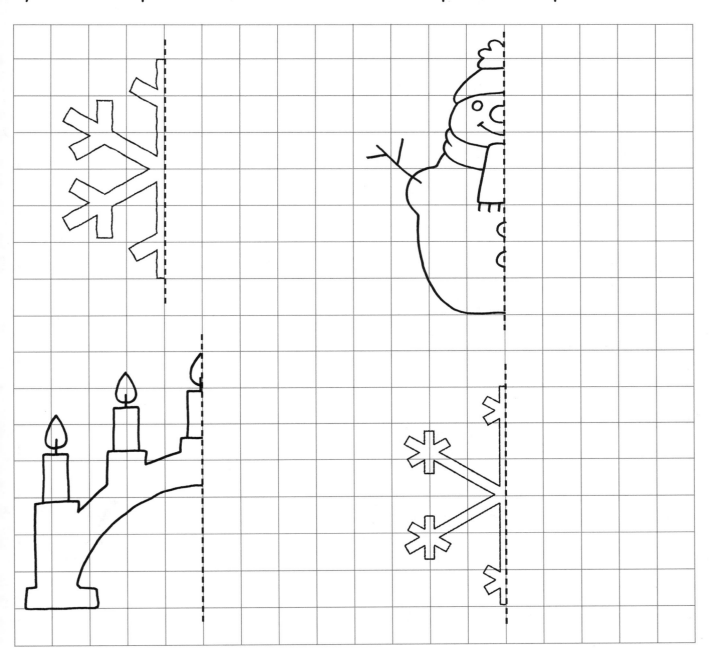

Colour the pictures you have made. Remember to follow the symmetry when you colour.

Notes for teachers

Objective: Sketch the reflection of a simple shape

Encourage children to count the squares to correctly measure the lines they need to draw. They should use a ruler for all straight lines. A mirror could be used for checking the results.

Symmetrical tree

Name:

 **Date:**

Look carefully at this half-completed Christmas tree. Draw the other half of the tree to make a totally symmetrical picture.

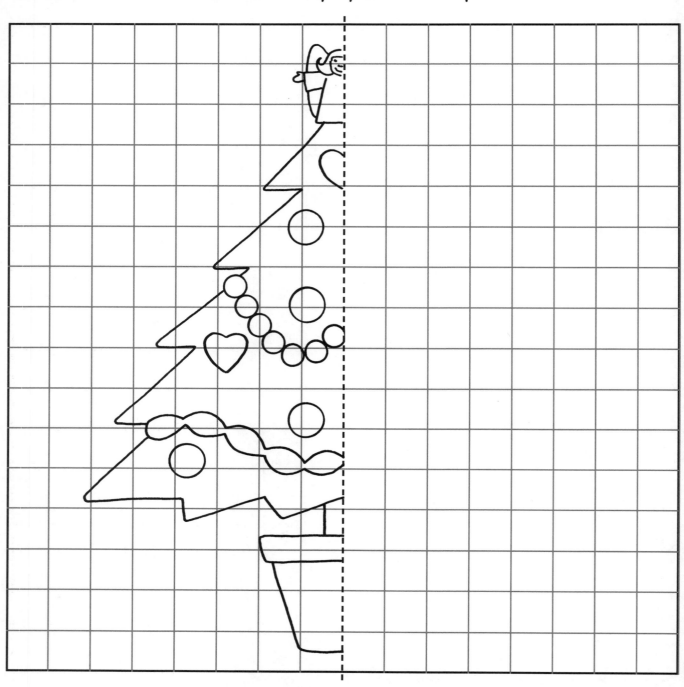

Notes for teachers
Objective: Sketch the reflection of a simple shape
Encourage children to count the squares to correctly measure the lines they need to draw. They should use a ruler for all straight lines. Drawing the curved lines may be more difficult and will require closer observation. Encourage the children to colour symmetrically i.e. if they colour a bauble in red on the left hand side of the mirror line, they must colour the reflected bauble red as well. A mirror could be used for checking the results.

Andrew Brodie: Christmas Maths 7–9 © A & C Black Publishers Ltd. 2006

My symmetry picture

Name:

Date:

Use the grid to draw your own symmetrical Christmas picture.

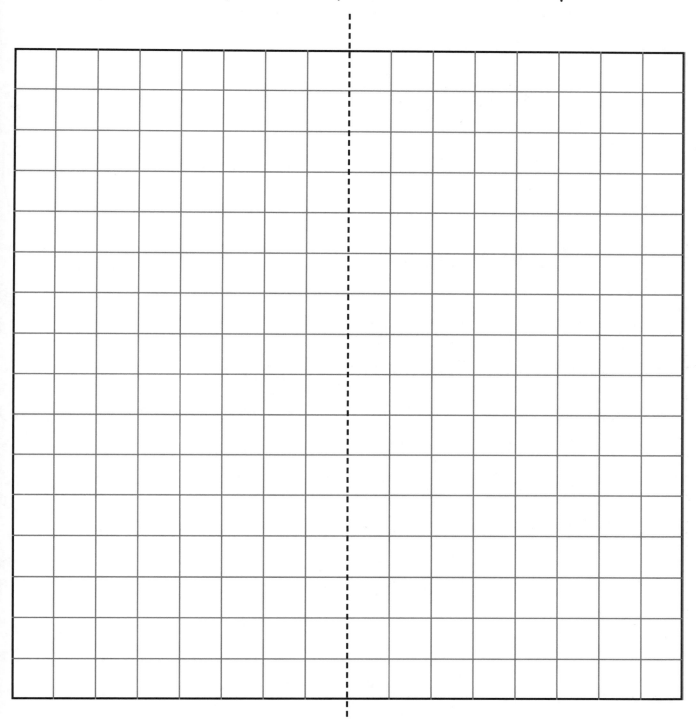

Notes for teachers

Objective: Sketch the reflection of a simple shape

Encourage children to count the squares to correctly measure the lines they need to draw. They should use a ruler for all straight lines. A mirror could be used for checking the results.

Order in the workshop (1)

Name:

 Date:

Santa's workshop is in rather a muddle. Help to sort it out by filling in the chart on Worksheet 24 to show how many of each toy has already been made.

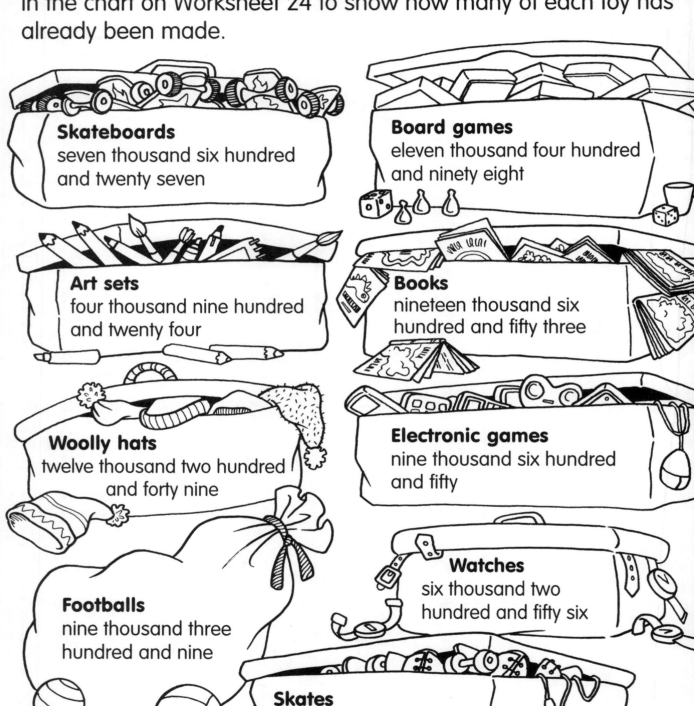

Skateboards
seven thousand six hundred and twenty seven

Board games
eleven thousand four hundred and ninety eight

Art sets
four thousand nine hundred and twenty four

Books
nineteen thousand six hundred and fifty three

Woolly hats
twelve thousand two hundred and forty nine

Electronic games
nine thousand six hundred and fifty

Footballs
nine thousand three hundred and nine

Watches
six thousand two hundred and fifty six

Skates
ten thousand and five

Notes for teachers
Objective: Read and write whole numbers to at least 10,000 in figures and words
This worksheet needs to be used in conjunction with Worksheet 24.

Andrew Brodie: Christmas Maths 7–9 © A & C Black Publishers Ltd. 2006

Order in the workshop (2)

Name:  **Date:**

Fill in the chart beginning with the smallest number. The first two have been done for you.

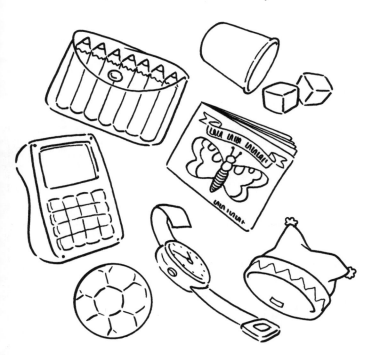

Item	Number
Art Sets	4,924
Watches	6,256

Now write these numbers in words:

6,479 ....

9,324 ....

4,038 ....

5,142 ....

7,584 ....

Notes for teachers
Objective: Read and write whole numbers to at least 10,000 in figures and words
An extension to this activity for the most able children would be to ask them to round the given numbers to the nearest 10 or 100 or 1,000.

Christmas rounding (1)

Name:

 Date:

The Christmas Shop needs to keep track of roughly how many decorations they have available for sale this year.

Write the decorations in order on the table on Worksheet 26, from the fewest to the most.

 Snowmen 994

 Reindeer 249

 Advent Candles 638

 Angels 702

 Robins 450

 Stars 495

 Tinsel 543

 Tree Lights 106

 Crackers 369

 Christmas Trees 65

 Baubles 811

 Santas 176

Notes for teachers

Objective: Round any positive integer less than 1,000 to the nearest ten or hundred

This worksheet needs to be used in conjunction with Worksheet 26. However, you could also make effective use of the sheet as a source of mathematical questions. For example, you could ask how many more snowmen there are than reindeer, or how many items there are on the page altogether, etc.

Christmas rounding (2)

Name: **Date:**

Write the decorations in order from the fewest to the most.

Complete the table by rounding to the nearest ten and the nearest hundred.

The first one has been done for you.

Item	Number	Rounded to nearest 10	Rounded to nearest 100
Christmas trees	65	70	100

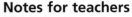

Notes for teachers
Objective: Round any positive integer less than 1000 to the nearest ten or hundred
An extension to this activity for the most able children would be for them to calculate how many more of each item would be needed for the shop to stock one thousand of each item.

Crack the code (1)

Name: **Date:**

Double each of the numbers below to crack the code and read the message.

Use the code to make a mystery Christmas message for a friend to solve.

11	26	47	17
22	52		

12	17	20

19	20	50

__W__ __I__ __ __ __ __ __ __ __ __ __ __

47	39	17	35	39	17	27	50	47

__ __ __ __ __ __ __ __ __

46	26	47	26	18	17	50

18	39	17

__ __ __ __ __ __ __   __ __ __

29	19	29	23

9	17	47	7	47

__ __ __ __   __ __ __ __ __

A	38
B	58
C	62
D	100
E	34
F	48
G	28
H	78
I	52
J	18
K	20
L	98
M	24
N	40
O	16
P	70
Q	42
R	54
S	94
T	36
U	14
V	92
W	22
X	76
Y	46
Z	26

Notes for teachers
Objective: Know the doubles of all whole numbers up to 50
The message should read 'Wise men and shepherds visited the baby Jesus.'

Andrew Brodie: Christmas Maths 7–9 © A & C Black Publishers Ltd. 2006

Crack the code (2)

Name: **Date:**

Halve each of the numbers below to crack the code and read the message.

Use the code to make a mystery Christmas message for a friend to solve.

A	29
B	24
C	35
D	19
E	49
F	37
G	27
H	21
I	50
J	13
K	44
L	38
M	26
N	36
O	47
P	20
Q	25
R	46
S	18
T	39
U	48
V	12
W	32
X	11
Y	42
Z	17

64	98
32	49

W   E

70	98	76	98	48	92	58	78	98

___ ___ ___ ___ ___ ___ ___ ___ ___

70	42	92	100	36	78	52	58	36

100	72

___ ___ ___ ___ ___ ___ ___ ___ ___   ___ ___

38	98	70	98	52	48	98	92

___ ___ ___ ___ ___ ___ ___ ___

Notes for teachers
Objective: Know the corresponding halves of all the doubles of numbers up to 50
The message should read 'We celebrate Christmas in December.'

Crazy trees

Name:  **Date:**

Look at the number on the pot of each tree.
Half of each tree that is in the 3 times table should be coloured red.
Half of each tree that is in the 6 times table should be coloured yellow.

What do you notice about the trees that you have coloured?
Now colour green the remaining trees and half trees.

- -

Notes for teachers
Objective: Know by heart multiplication facts for the three times table and begin to know multiplication facts for the six times table
The numbering of these trees has been arranged randomly to give pupils maximum tables practice. To gain the most from this activity pupils should have seen that each six is two threes. They might also notice that the numbers that occur in both tables are even numbers whereas tree ones that are only in the three times table are odd numbers. An extension to this activity is to ask pupils to colour the stars orange if the tree belongs to the 4 times table.

Andrew Brodie: Christmas Maths 7–9 © A & C Black Publishers Ltd. 2006

Christmas tree tables

Name:  **Date:**

Colour red all the baubles that are in the 7 times table.
Colour yellow all the lights that are in the 4 times table.

Notes for teachers

Objective: Begin to know multiplication facts for the seven times table and know by heart the multiplication facts for the four times table

This sheet can be used for consolidation of the 4 times table and as an aid to learning the 7 times table. You could ask the pupils which number is in the 4 times table and the 7 times table, reminding the children of the term 'multiple'.

Ring out the bells

Name: **Date:**

Look at the bells below.

Colour half the bell yellow if it belongs in the 4 times table.

Colour half the bell red if it belongs in the 8 times table.

Draw around the outside of the bell in blue if it belongs to the 6 times table.

What do you notice about the bells you have coloured? _____

Notes for teachers
Objective: Know by heart multiplication facts for the four times table and begin to know the six and eight times tables Pupils should clearly see the pattern emerging in the colouring of the bells.

     Andrew Brodie: Christmas Maths 7–9 © A & C Black Publishers Ltd. 2006

Santa's little helpers

Name:  **Date:**

Santa's little helpers all look the same. He needs a group of them to load the sleigh. He chooses all the helpers in the nine times table.

Colour in the helpers who are going to load Santa's sleigh.

See how quickly you can write out your nine times table.
You could use a clock with a second hand to time yourself.

Notes for teachers
Objective: Begin to know multiplication facts for the 9 times table
An additional activity would be to ask the pupils to write the numbers of the nine times table in order and to look for any details they notice that could help them to learn the table easily, e.g. the ascending tens and the descending units.

Fraction baubles

Name:

 **Date:**

Follow the instructions to colour each bauble correctly.

Colour $\frac{1}{2}$ blue	Colour 0.2 green
Colour $\frac{3}{10}$ red	Colour 0.5 purple
Colour 0.6 green	Colour $\frac{6}{10}$ pink
Colour $\frac{1}{5}$ blue	Colour 0.8 yellow
Colour 0.4 orange	Colour $\frac{4}{10}$ red

Notes for teachers
Objective: Begin to relate fractions to division and find simple fractions, to use fraction notation and understand decimal notation, and to recognise the equivalence between the decimal and fraction forms of one half and one quarter and tenths.
The specified colours have no particular significance to the exercise so pupils can substitute other colours if necessary.
To extend this activity, substitute other fractions and decimals for those given to best match the level of individual pupils.

Andrew Brodie: Christmas Maths 7–9 © A & C Black Publishers Ltd. 2006

Parcel sorting (1)

Name:  **Date:**

The parcels need sorting ready to be loaded onto the sleigh.
Sort them into the sacks according to the area of the side view
of each parcel. The first one has been done for you.

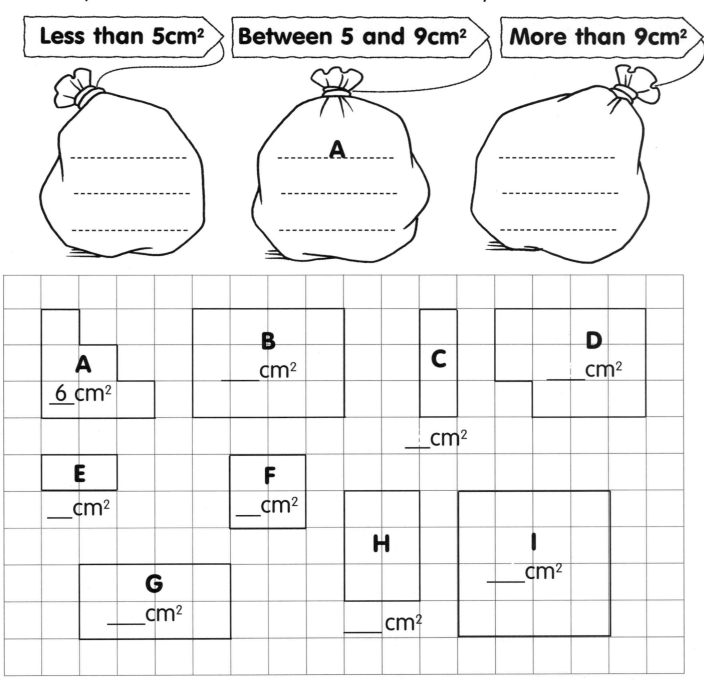

| Less than 5cm² | Between 5 and 9cm² | More than 9cm² |

A

A
6 cm²

B
__ cm²

C

D
__ cm²

__ cm²

E
__ cm²

F
__ cm²

H

I
__ cm²

G
__ cm²

__ cm²

Notes for teachers

Objective: Calculate the area of rectangles and other simple shapes

Pupils will need to find the area of each shape by counting the square centimetres. An extension to this activity would be
to ask pupils to cut out the shapes and find out what would be the smallest rectangular sleigh that could accommodate
all the parcels without any of them overlapping.

Worksheet 35 Parcel sorting (2)

Name: **Date:**

Find the area of each parcel. Fill in the table below putting the Christmas parcels in order of area starting with the smallest. The first one has been done for you.

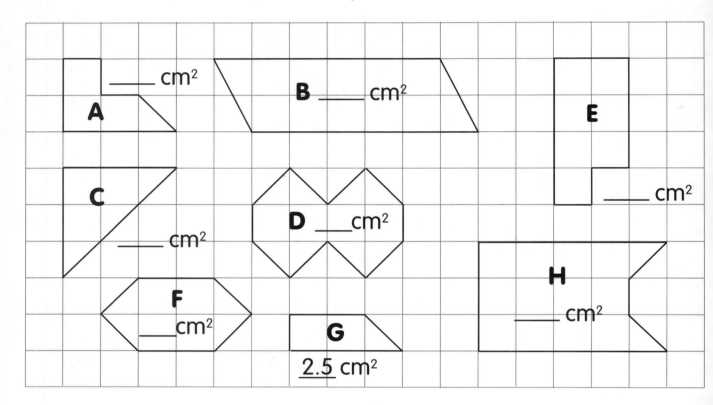

Parcel	Area
G	2.5 cm²
	cm²
	cm²
	cm²

Parcel	Area
	cm²
	cm²
	cm²
	cm²

Now draw six differently shaped parcels all with an area of 12.5 cm². You will need to do this on squared paper.

Notes for teachers
Objective: Calculate the area of rectangles and other simple shapes
Ensure pupils realise that there are half squares included in this, so for each shape they can calculate the area of the square or rectangle and then add the additional triangular half squares. When working on the extension activity pupils may be encouraged to realise that any one square centimetre could be halved vertically, horizontally or diagonally.

Label the presents

Name:  Date:

Use the clues below to match the correct present to its owner.
Write the owner's name on the label.

- Joe's parcel has 3 right angles.
- Lea's present is rectangular with a perimeter of 12 cm.
- Matthew's parcel has no right angles and only one straight edge.
- Jordan will be receiving a package with 4 right angles and the greatest perimeter of all the parcels.
- Max's parcel has 7 straight edges but only two right angles.
- Sam's rectangular present has a perimeter of 14 cm.
- Tara's parcel has 4 right angles and a perimeter of 8 cm.
- Larry's parcel has no straight edges or right angles.

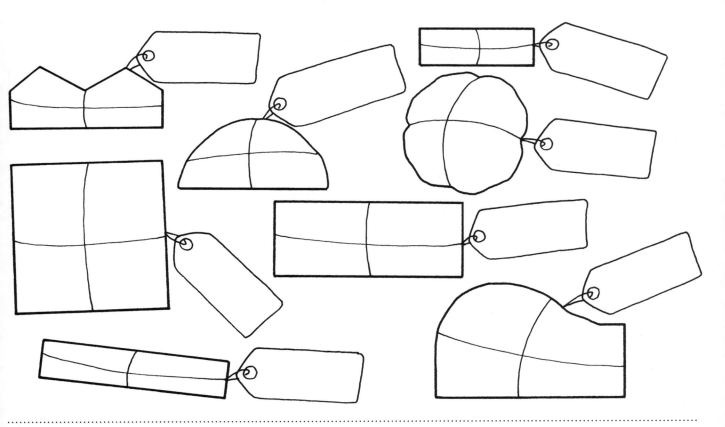

Notes for teachers
Objective: Calculate the perimeter of rectangles and other simple shapes and classify polygons using criteria such as number of right angles
Many children confuse area with perimeter and will need reminding that the perimeter of a shape is the distance all the way round it.

Christmas shopping (1)

Name:  **Date:**

Kim decides to go Christmas shopping. She has a five pound note.

For each item in the table below calculate how much change Kim would get if she bought it with her five pound note.

Item		Price	Change from £5
book		£2.50	
pencil sharpener		£1.25	
ruler		95p	
bracelet		£3.20	
mug		£4.30	
pack of three pencils		85p	
toy snowman		£2.75	

Kim wants to buy three presents. Which three presents could she buy by spending exactly £5? ....

Notes for teachers
Objective: Use subtraction and addition to solve problems with money
Encourage the children to 'count on' when finding change. Many children are likely to give the answer £2.80 when finding the change from £5 for spending £3.20. Counting on from £3.20 to £5 avoids this difficulty. Finding the three items that cost exactly £5 altogether is a challenging problem and will involve addition and subtraction.

Christmas shopping (2)

Name:  Date:

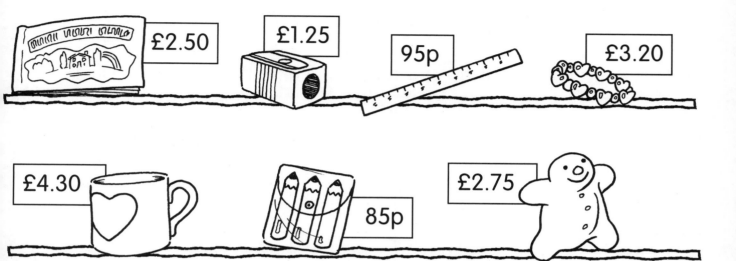

£2.50 £1.25 95p £3.20

£4.30 85p £2.75

Answer these questions.

1. What is the total cost of three books?

2. What is the total cost of four bracelets?

3. What is the total cost of two pencil sharpeners?

4. What is the total cost of three packs of pencils?

5. What would be the total cost of one of each item?

6. Kim decides to buy one of each item but to share the cost with her three brothers. How much would they each have to pay to carry out Kim's plan?

.....

Notes for teachers

Objective: Use addition, multiplication and division to solve problems with money
The final division question is the most challenging. The children should have found that the total bill if Kim buys each item will be £15.80. They need to realise that they will have to divide by four not three. You may like to ask them whether they think Kim's brothers will agree to her plan!

My December calendar

Name: _____   Date: _____

December

Sunday	Monday	Tuesday	Wednesday	Thursday	Friday	Saturday

What day of the week is 1st December this year? _____

Write the number 1 in the correct square on the top row to show 1st December. Now write the numbers 2 to 31 in the correct squares.

What day of the week will Christmas Day be this year? _____

Notes for teachers
Objective: Understand time on calendars and spell days of the week
Many children will not realise that Christmas Day falls on different days of the week. This activity will raise their understanding of how a calendar is organised. Their first task is to find out what day of the week 1st December falls on this year. They could do this by counting on or back from today's date or by looking it up on a calendar, in a diary or on the internet. The children will use their calendar page when working on sheet 40.

December dates

Name:  **Date:**

Look at your calendar page on Worksheet 39, then answer these questions.

1. What is the date exactly
one week before Christmas? --

2. What is the date exactly
two weeks before Christmas? --

3. What is the date exactly
three weeks before Christmas? --

4. What is the date exactly
one week after Christmas? --

5. What is the date today? --

6. How many days are there
from now until Christmas? --

7. How many weeks and days is this? --

8. How many days are there from
now until the first day of next year? --

9. How many weeks and days is this? --

Notes for teachers

Objective: Understand time on calendars

This activity will help children to realise that the new year is exactly one week after Christmas Day. Finding how many weeks and days there are from one date to another involves subtraction and division with remainders. For example, if the date is 2nd December there are twenty-three days to Christmas (25 – 2): this is three weeks and two days (23 ÷ 7 = 3 remainder 2). The best ways for pupils to observe these operations is to complete them by counting on the calendar.

Christmas stars

Name:  **Date:**

Look how you can draw a star.

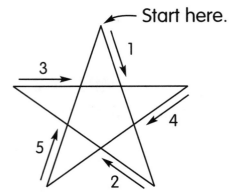

Can you continue this pattern?

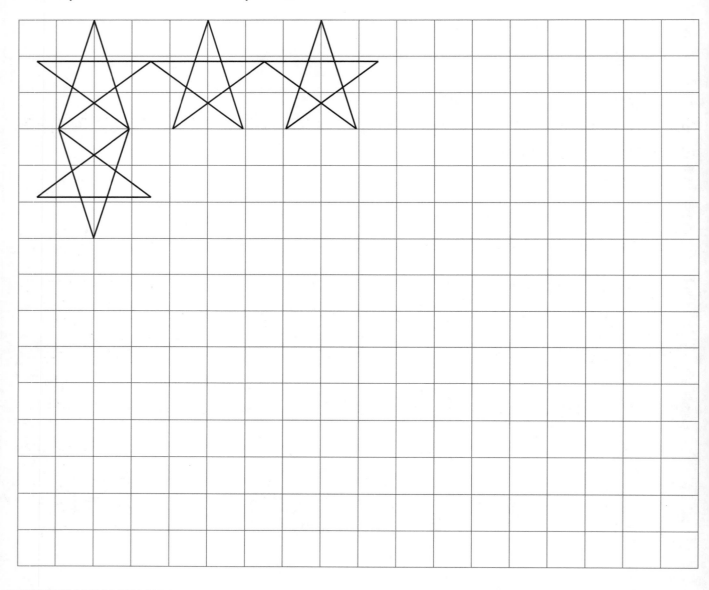

Notes for teachers
Objective: Make patterns by translation and reflection
This is a surprisingly difficult task for many children – encourage them to use pencils and rulers and allow them to erase incorrect attempts.

Finding triangles

Name: **Date:**

How many triangles can you find in this star?

Here are some extra stars so that you can colour in all the triangles you find on separate stars.

Notes for teachers

Objective: Solve mathematical puzzles

The extra stars are provided so that children can colour a different triangle in each one. They should be able to find ten different triangles.

Finding pentagons

Name:

 Date:

How many pentagons can you find in this star?

Here are some extra stars so that you can colour in all the pentagons you find on separate stars.

Notes for teachers
Objective: Solve mathematical puzzles and describe and visualise 2-D shapes
Children will need to appreciate that the pentagon does not have to be a regular shape. The central pentagon is the easy one to find but there are several more.

How many shapes?

Name:  **Date:**

How many different shapes can you find in this star?

Here are some extra stars so that you can colour in all the shapes you find on separate stars.

Notes for teachers
Objective: To solve mathematical puzzles
Again, the shapes do not need to be regular. The different shapes that the children will be able to find include: triangle, quadrilateral, pentagon, hexagon, heptagon and decagon.

worksheet 45

Christmas Su Doku

Name: Date:

Every box must have a

Every row must have a

Every column must have a

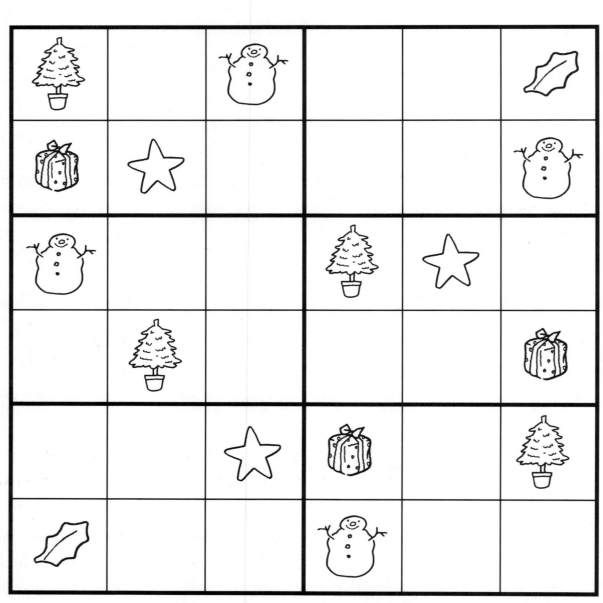

Can you fill all the squares?

Notes for teachers
Objective: Solve mathematical puzzles
Encourage the children to colour each of the Christmas symbols differently so that it will be easier for them to fill the gaps

Andrew Brodie: Christmas Maths 7–9 © A & C Black Publishers Ltd. 2006